Status Quo

GUITAR LEGENDS

ROCKIN' ALL OVER THE WORLD	2
WHATEVER YOU WANT	8
WHAT YOU'RE PROPOSING	17
MARGUERITA TIME	22
IN THE ARMY NOW	26
BURNING BRIDGES	31
LIKE IT OR NOT	37
QUEENIE	43
NOTATION AND TABLATURE EXPLAINED	49

© International Music Publications Ltd
First published in 2000 by International Music Publications Ltd
International Music Publications Ltd is a Faber Music company
Bloomsbury House 74–77 Great Russell Street London WC1B 3DA
Music arranged and processed by Barnes Music Engraving Ltd
Cover design by xheight design limited
Printed in England by Caligraving Ltd
All rights reserved

ISBN10: 0-571-52914-3
EAN13: 978-0-571-52914-8

To buy Faber Music publications or to find out about the full range of titles available,
please contact your local music retailer or Faber Music sales enquiries:

Faber Music Ltd, Burnt Mill, Elizabeth Way, Harlow, CM20 2HX England
Tel: +44(0)1279 82 89 82   Fax: +44(0)1279 82 89 83
sales@fabermusic.com   fabermusic.com

ROCKIN' ALL OVER THE WORLD

Words and Music by John Fogerty

For over 30 years Status Quo has been one of Britain's most consistently successful rock bands. Status Quo officially came into existance in 1967 although several members of the band had been playing together as far back as 1962.

The track *Rocking All Over The World* has become one of Quo's best-loved anthems. Written by Credence Clearwater Revival's John Fogerty and released by Quo in 1977, the song remained in the UK charts for 16 weeks and reached number 3.

Quo were chosen to open the 1985 *Live Aid* event at Wembley Stadium with this number, and they also recorded a re-worked version *Running All Over The World* in 1988 for charity.

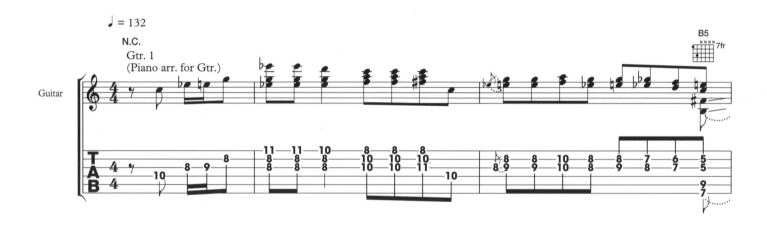

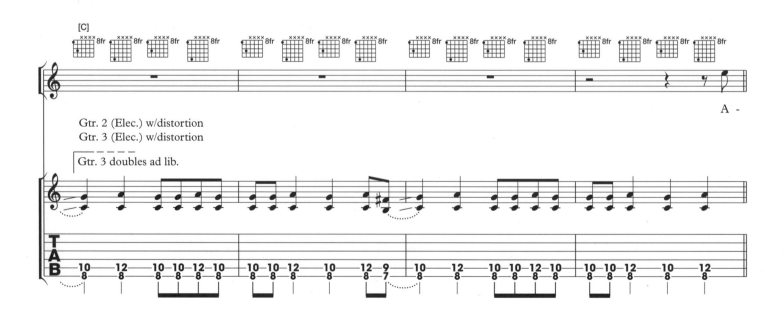

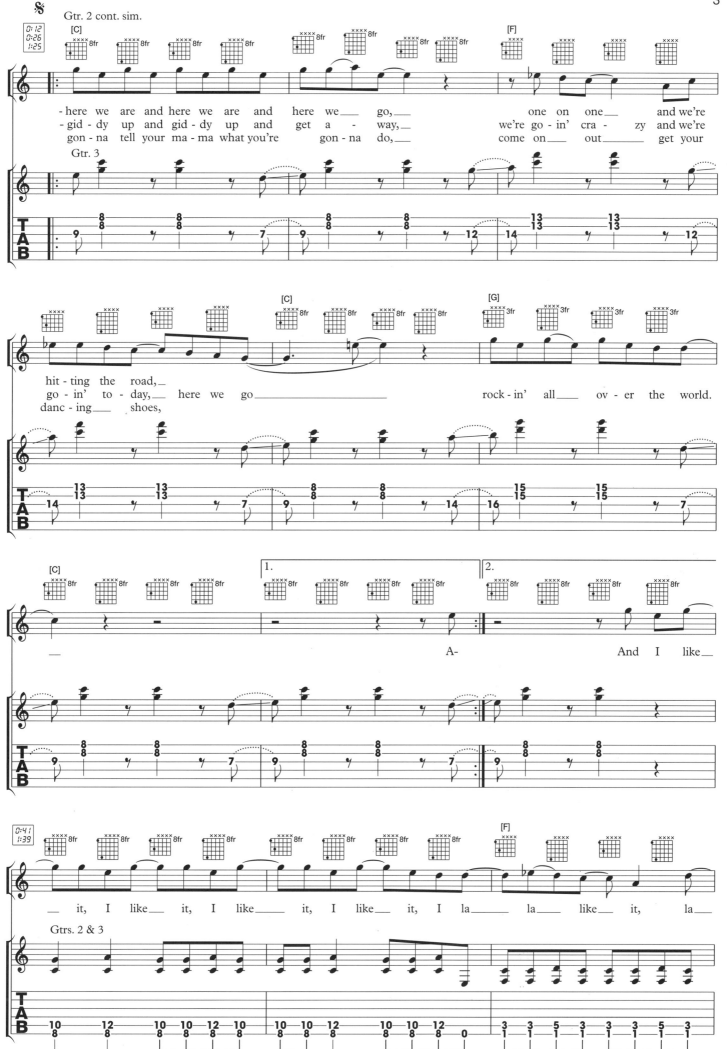

4

la___ like,___ here we go_____ rock-in' all___ ov-er the world.

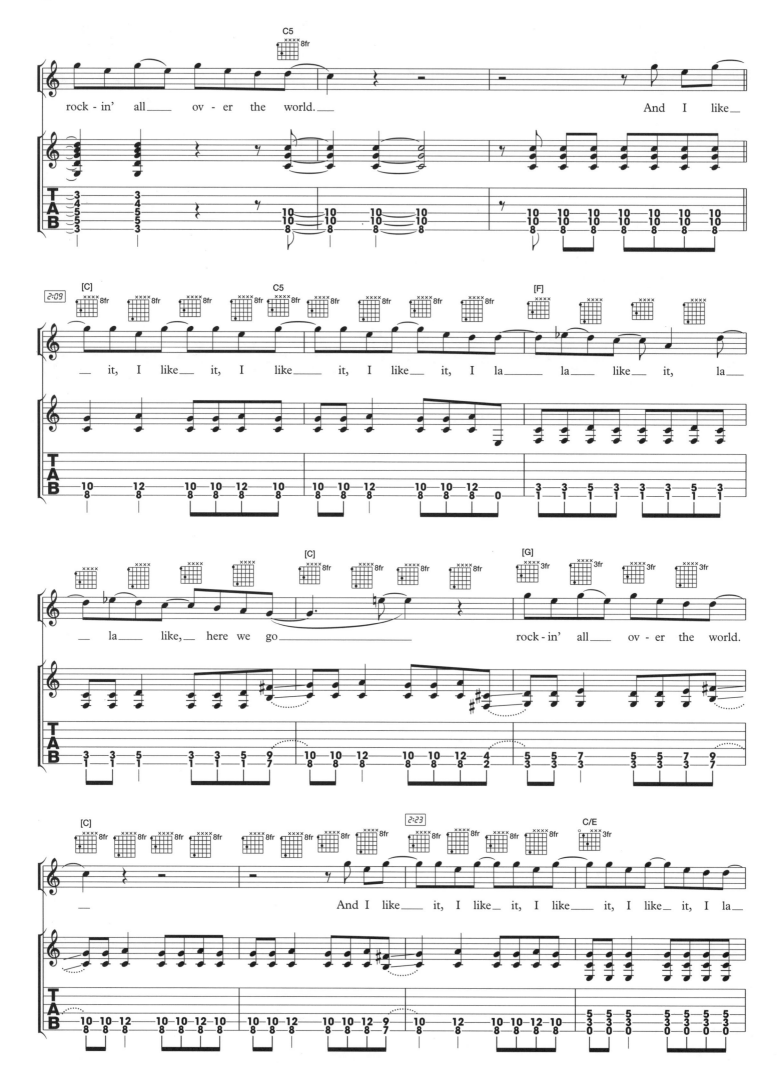

WHATEVER YOU WANT

Words and Music by Andy Bown and Richard Parfitt

Throughout their long history, Status Quo have undergone several personnel changes, but the core of the band has always been Francis Rossi (lead guitar and vocals) and Rick Parfitt (rhythm guitar and vocals).

In 1979, the year *Whatever You Want* was recorded, the line up was Francis, Rick, Alan Lancaster (bass and vocals), John Coghlan (drums) and Andy Bown (keyboard and backing vocals). Bown replaced original member Roy Lynes.

Whatever You Want, penned by Parfitt and Bown is an irresistibly catchy song, evidenced by its use in several TV commercials! It builds from Rick's instantly recognisable solo guitar introduction into the main riff which drives the song. Taken from the album of the same name, the single peaked at number 4 in the UK charts.

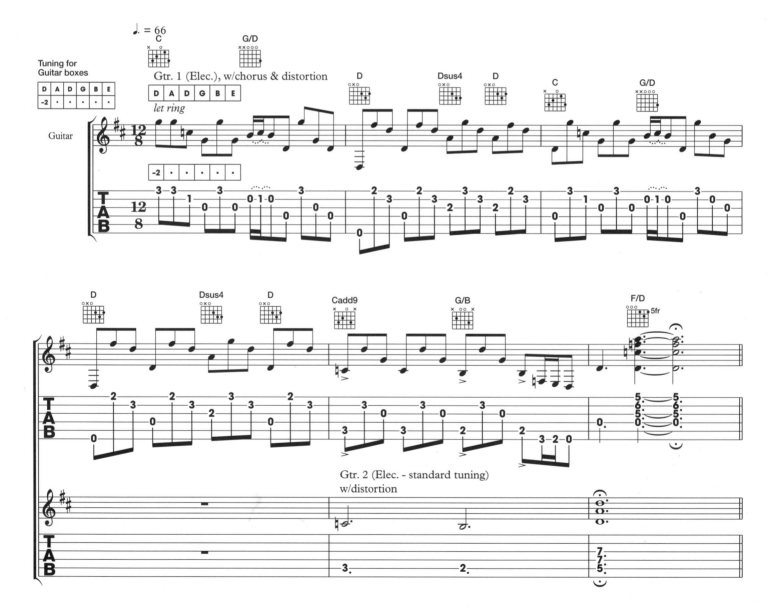

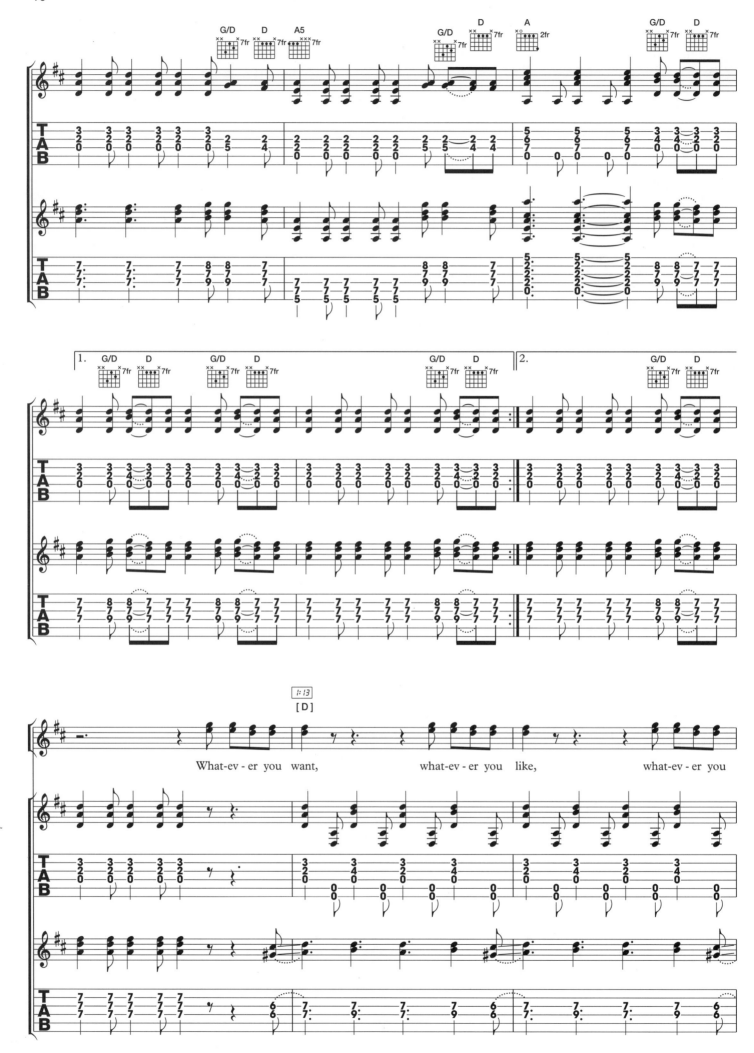

What-ev-er you want, what-ev-er you like, what-ev-er you

choice. What-ev-er you need, what-ev-er you use, what-ev-er you

win, what-ev-er you lose. _____

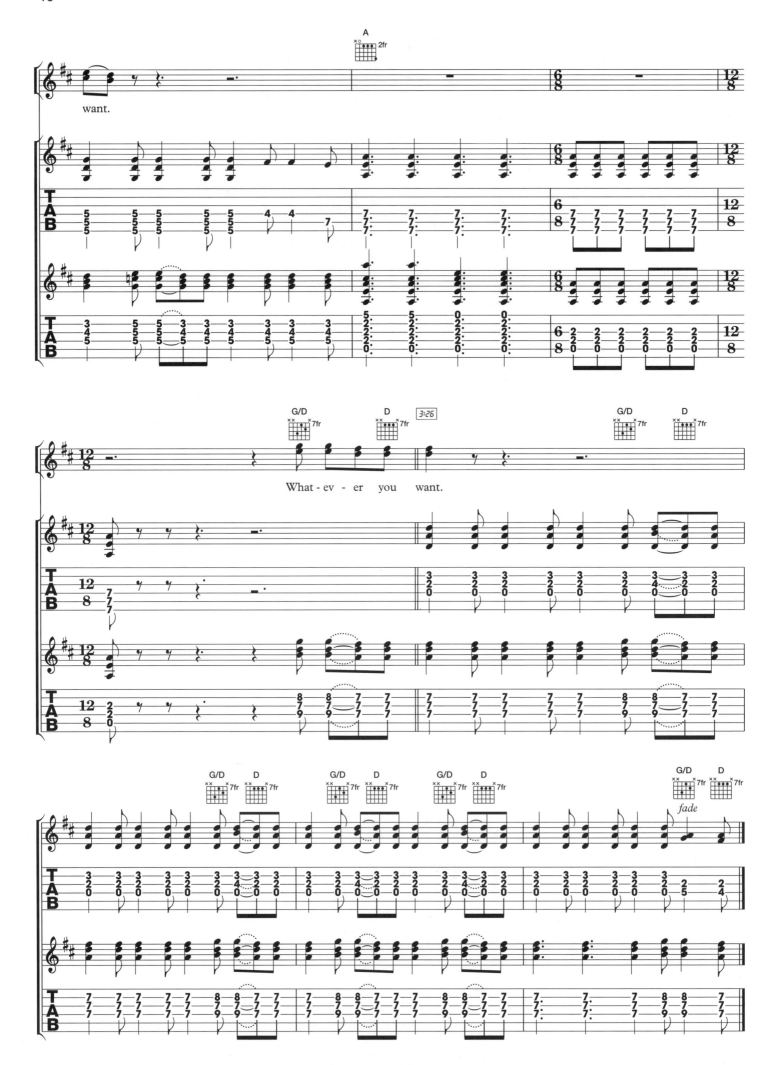

WHAT YOU'RE PROPOSING

Words and Music by Bernard Frost and Francis Rossi

Status Quo first achieved chart success in 1968 with the top 10 hits *Pictures Of Matchstick Men* and *Ice In The Sun*. The Quo of the late '60s was markedly different to the band of today, sporting elegantly coiffured hair and velvet suits with lace trim. Their music was perhaps typical of the pop/psychedelic music of the day.

However the 1970s saw the band change direction sharply by adopting the longhaired, denim-clad, no nonsense rock and roll image that has become their trademark. A good example of this is the 1980 hit *What You're Proposing*, taken from the album *JUST SUPPOSING*. The single reached number 2 in the UK charts.

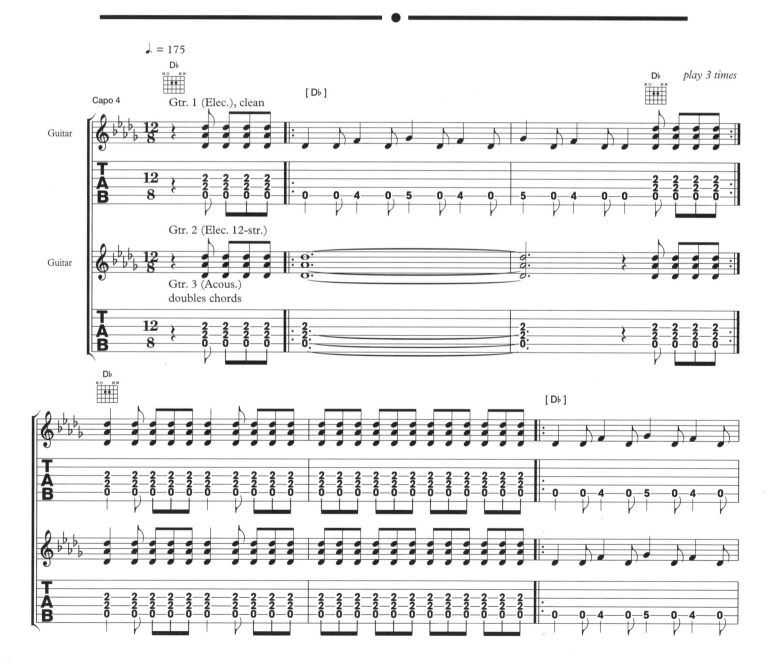

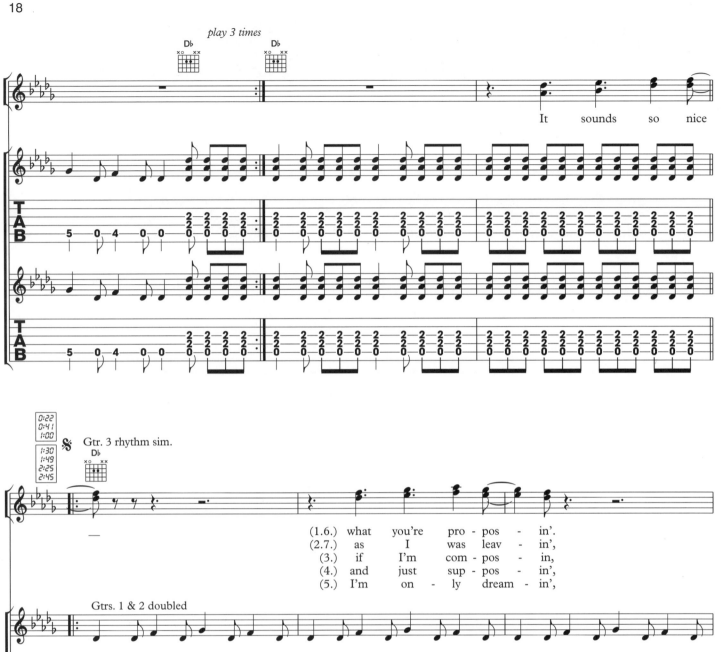

MARGUERITA TIME

Words and Music by Bernard Frost and Francis Rossi

Throughout the 1970s Quo had a string of single and album successes with their record company, Vertigo; for example *Paper Plane*, *Caroline*, *Break The Rules*, *Down Down*, and *Again And Again*.

Part of the band's attraction stemmed from their unpretentious attitude (a marked difference from many of their contemporaries) and the fact that their audience related to them as 'ordinary blokes'. They also toured frequently, allowing the fans to get close to them.

The 1983 release *Marguerita Time* was considered by some to be an odd choice for a single because of its lighter, 'poppier' style. However it went on to be a hit, reaching number 3 in the UK charts and gaining the band airplay both on rock and MOR radio stations.

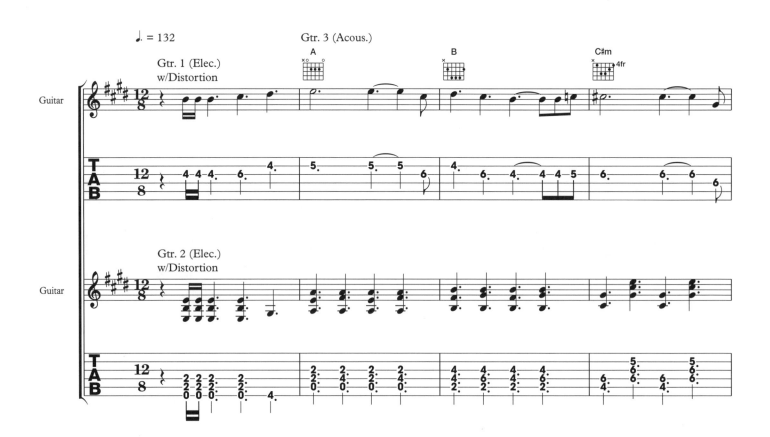

that I__ could be just like a - ny - one else. I'll take my chance with you.

Pic - ture__ a

Let's have a

IN THE ARMY NOW

Words and Music by Rob Bolland and Ferdi Bolland

The early 1980s were a period of mixed fortunes for the band. Long-time drummer John Coghlan left to form his own band *Diesel* and was replaced by former *Original Mirrors* drummer Pete Kircher.

1982 saw Quo celebrate the 20th anniversary of Francis and Alan Lancaster's meeting with the release of the *1+9+8+2(=20!)* album and a series of high profile gigs. They became the first rock band to play for royalty when Prince Charles and Princess Diana attended their concert at the Birmingham NEC in aid of the Prince's Trust.

In The Army Now was written in 1982 by the Dutch brothers Rob and Ferdi Bolland. Francis heard the single on a pirate radio station and liked it sufficiently to suggest that the band record it at some point. It wasn't until 1986 when a Quo rendition of the song surfaced, charting for 14 weeks and peaking at number 2.

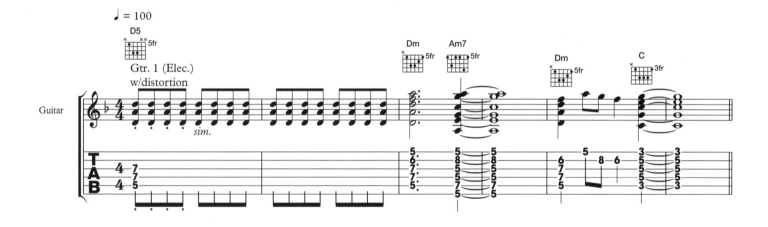

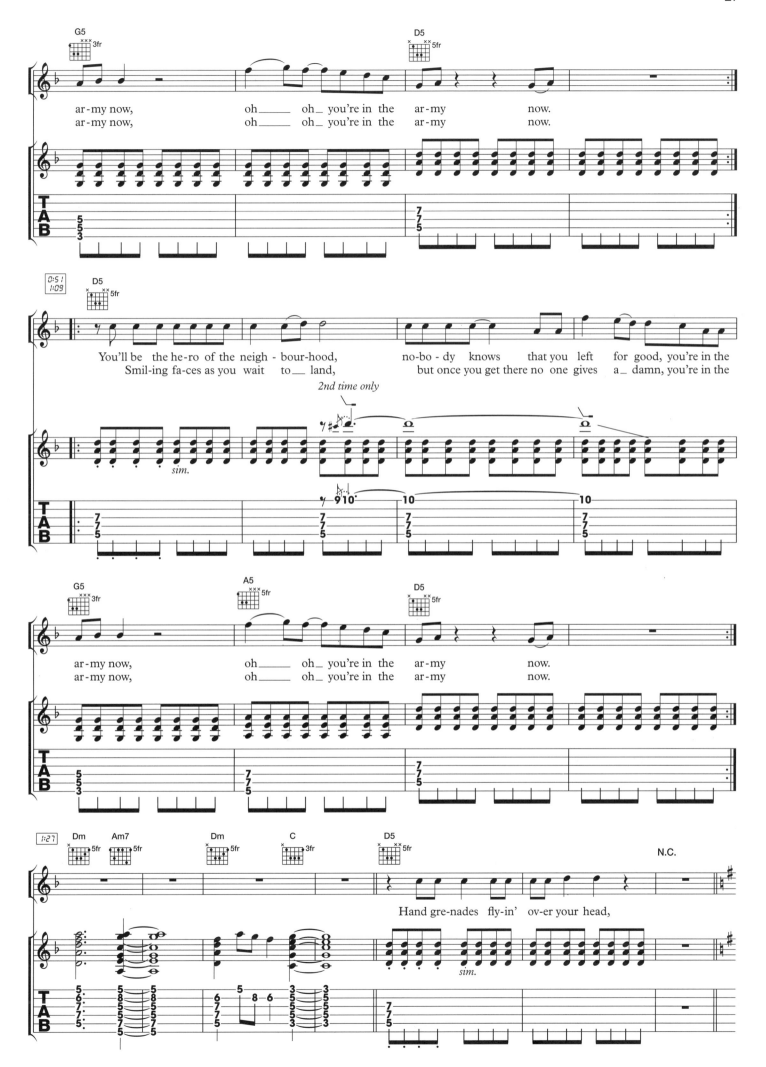

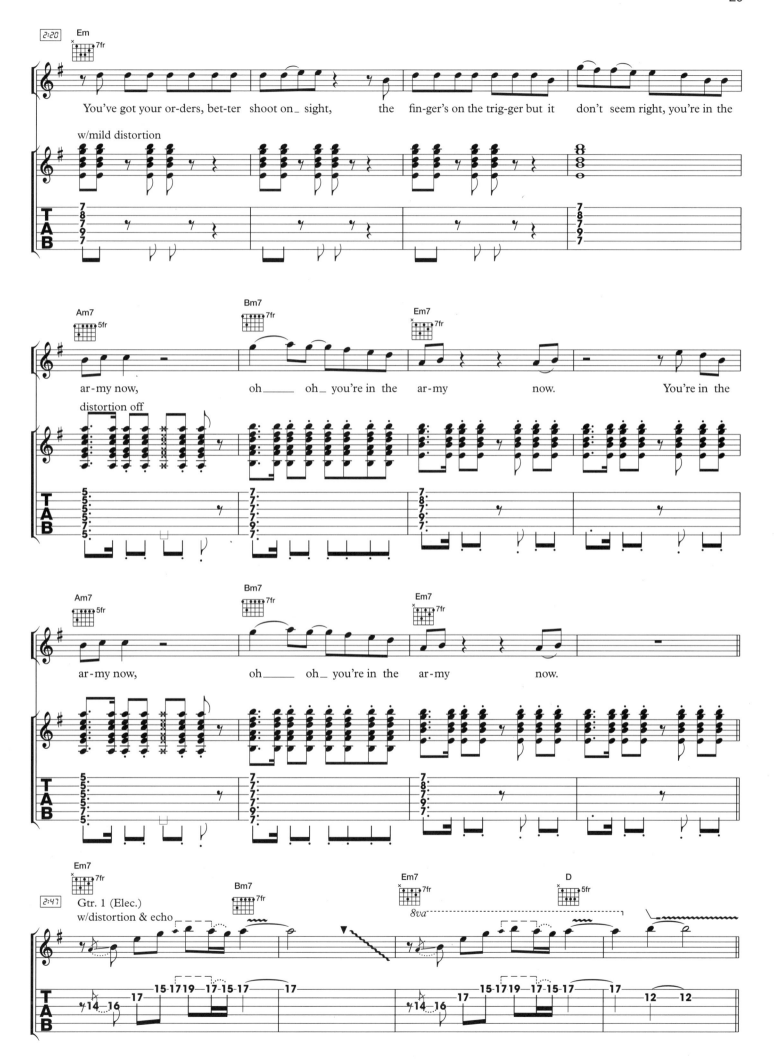

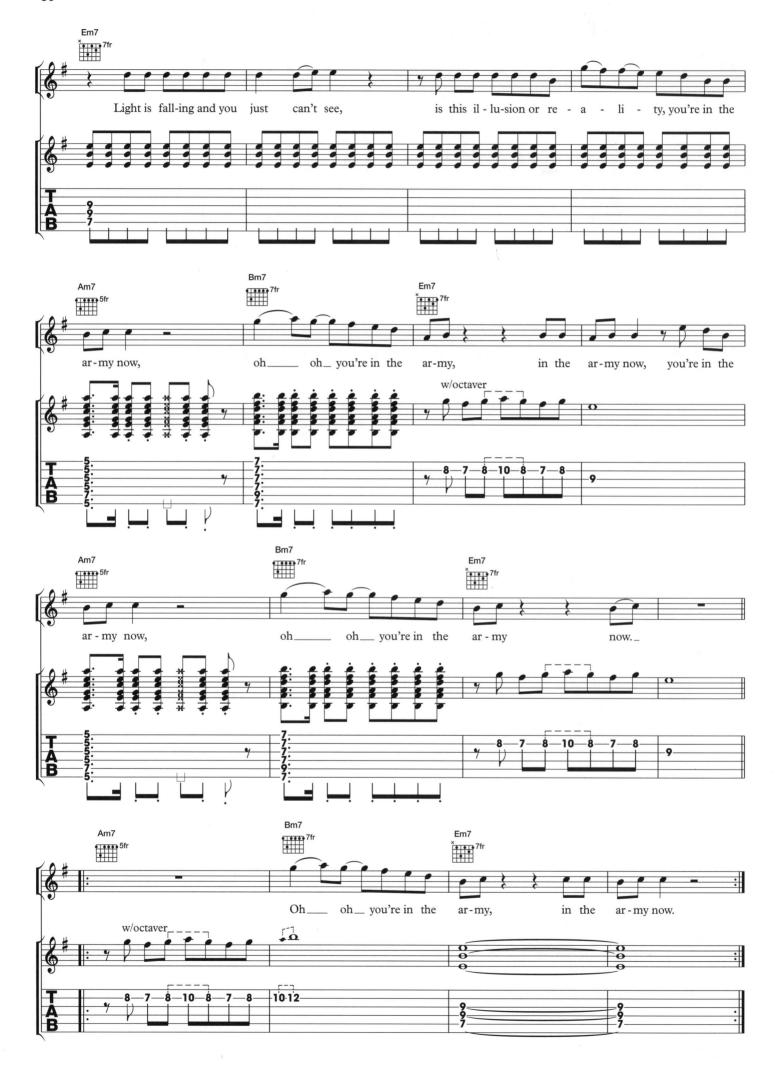

BURNING BRIDGES

Words and Music by Francis Rossi and Andy Bown

In 1984 Quo launched into the *End Of The Road* tour. The line-up at this point was Francis, Rick, Andy Bown and Pete Kircher. At the time people were wondering if this really was the end of Status Quo, and legions of fans showed up to give the band a good send off. The tour climaxed on 21st July 1984 with a huge concert at the Milton Keynes Bowl which spawned two live videos.

Burning Bridges was another surprise hit for Quo in 1988. Written by Francis Rossi and Andy Bown, the tune was based on the traditional Irish melody *Derby Kelly*. The record company put the band under some pressure to drop this track from the album *AIN'T COMPLAININ'*, until they saw how the fans responded to it so positively at live gigs.

In 1994 the band re-worked the track for Manchester United FC as *Come On You Reds* which charted at number one.

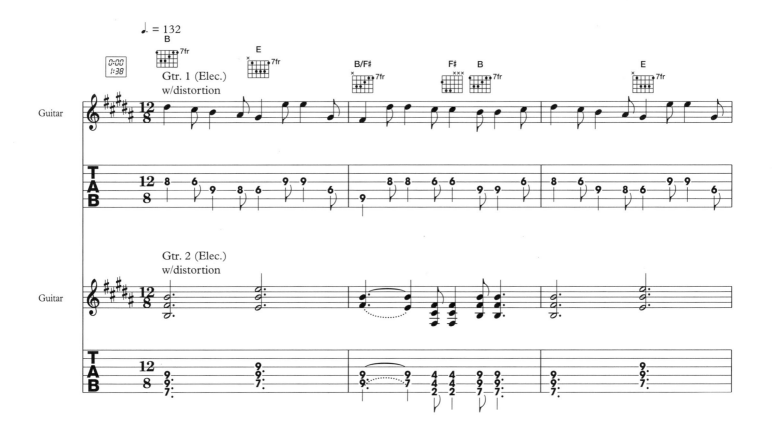

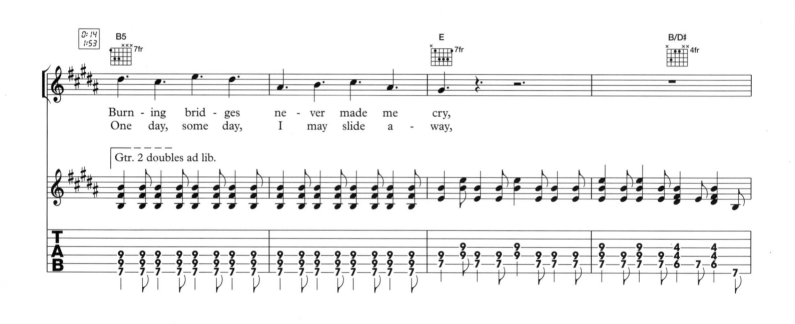

Burn - ing brid - ges ne - ver made me cry,
One day, some day, I may slide a - way,

Gtr. 2 doubles ad lib.

I could walk a - way with no good - bye.
turn a - round and call it all a ___ day.

34

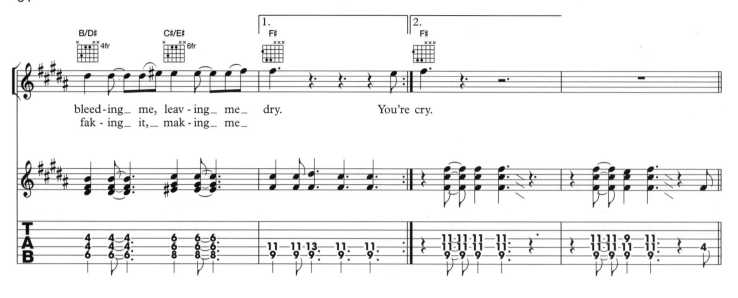

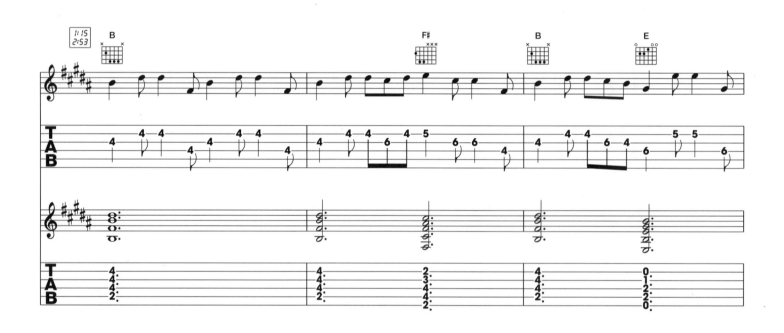

LIKE IT OR NOT

Words and Music by Francis Rossi and Damon Frost

Alan Lancaster was becoming increasingly unhappy with what he saw as the band's shift away from rock towards commercialism. After periods of discord and reconciliation, Lancaster eventually left in 1985 and took out a high court injunction to prevent the rest of the band playing under the Status Quo name. The courts found in favour of Rossi and Parfitt.

Like It Or Not, taken from the 1994 album *Thirsty Work* is a mid-paced rock shuffle which sees the band returning to its rock roots.

Is-n't it

more the way you do it than the way that you look? Is-n't it

in the way you use it not the les-sons you took? Is-n't it

time we start-ed ask-ing what goes on in your mind?

ain't gon-na stop. We're in a stick-y si-tu-a-tion and you real-ly don't mind.

repeat ad lib. to fade

QUEENIE

Words and Music by Francis Rossi and Damon Frost

With the court case behind them Quo reformed in 1986 for the album *IN THE ARMY NOW*. Joining Francis, Rick and Andy Bown were bassist John 'Rhino' Edwards and drummer Jeff Rich. It soon became obvious that the band were enjoying themselves again and a string of successful albums, singles and tours followed.

In 1991 the band were awarded a prestigious BRIT award for Outstanding Contribution to the British Music Industry. When collecting their award the band wore formal dinner jackets, only to rip them off to reveal their trademark jeans and t-shirts underneath.

The 1994 track *Queenie* shows that Quo have lost none of their drive and energy, giving the hope that they will still be rocking for many years to come.

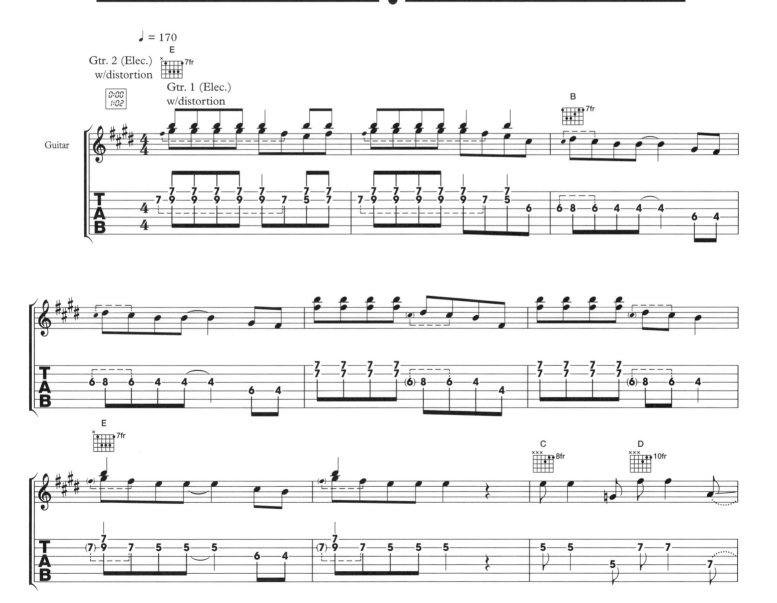

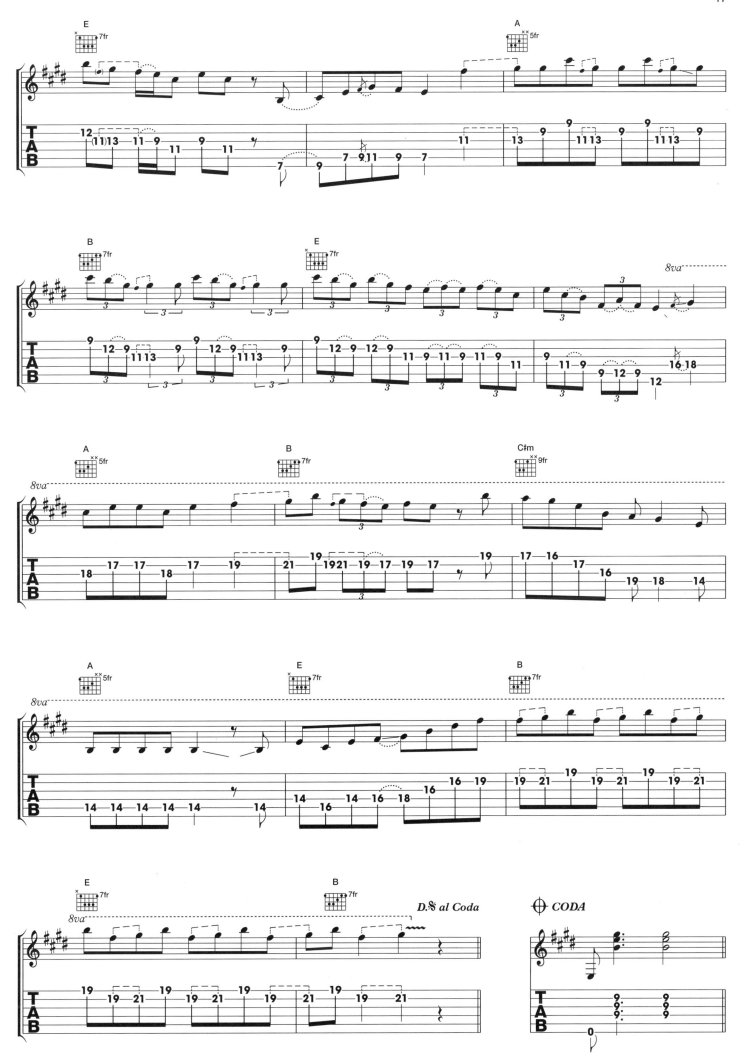

Queen-ie, Queen-ie, Queen-ie, won't__ you come a-long and make a home with me.__

Queen-ie, Queen-ie, Queen-ie, we__ could set-tle down and make some his-to-ry.__

repeat to fade

Notation and Tablature Explained

Open C chord

Scale of E major

High E (1st) string
B (2nd) string
G (3rd) string
D (4th) string
A (5th) string
Low E (6th) string

Bent Notes

The note fretted is always shown first. Variations in pitch achieved by string bending are enclosed within this symbol ⌐ ¬. If you aren't sure how far to bend the string, playing the notes indicated without bending gives a guide to the pitches to aim for. The following examples cover the most common string bending techniques:

Example 1
Play the D, bend up one tone (two half-steps) to E.

Example 4
Pre-bend: fret the D, bend up one tone to E, then pick.

Example 2
Play the D, bend up one tone to E then release bend to sound D. Only the first note is picked.

Example 5
Play the A and D together, then bend the B-string up one tone to sound B.

Example 3
Fast bend: Play the D, then bend up one tone to E as quickly as possible.

Example 6
Play the D and F♯ together, then bend the G-string up one tone to E, and the B-string up a semitone to G.

Additional guitaristic techniques have been notated as follows:

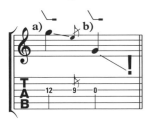

Tremolo Bar
Alter pitch using tremolo bar. Where possible, the pitch to aim for is shown.
a) Play the G; use the bar to drop the pitch to E.
b) Play the open G; use the bar to 'divebomb', i.e. drop the pitch as far as possible.

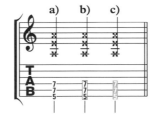

Mutes
a) Right hand mute
Mute strings by resting the right hand on the strings just above the bridge.
b) Left hand mute
Damp the strings by releasing left hand pressure just after the notes sound.
c) Unpitched mute
Damp the strings with the left hand to produce a percussive sound.

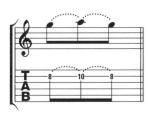

Hammer on and Pull off
Play first note, sound next note by 'hammering on', the next by 'pulling off'. Only the first note is picked.

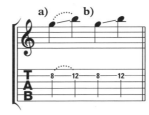

Glissando
a) Play first note, sound next note by sliding up string. Only the first note is picked.
b) As above, but pick second note.

Natural Harmonics
Touch the string over the fret marked, and pick to produce a bell-like tone. The small notes show the resultant pitch, where necessary.

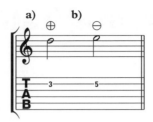

Slide Guitar
a) Play using slide.
b) Play without slide.

Artificial Harmonics
Fret the lowest note, touch string over fret indicated by diamond notehead and pick. Small notes show the resultant pitch.

Vibrato
Apply vibrato, by 'shaking' note or with tremolo bar. As vibrato is so much a matter of personal taste and technique, it is indicated only where essential.

Pinch Harmonics
Fret the note as usual, but 'pinch' or 'squeeze' the string with the picking hand to produce a harmonic overtone. Small notes show the resultant pitch.

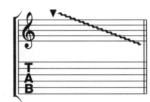

Pick Scratch
Scrape the pick down the strings – this works best on the wound strings.

Microtones
A downwards arrow means the written pitch is lowered by less than a semitone; an upwards arrow raises the written pitch.

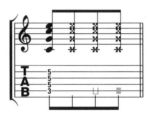

Repeated Chords
To make rhythm guitar parts easier to read the tablature numbers may be omitted when a chord is repeated. The example shows a C major chord played naturally, r/h muted, l/h muted and as an unpitched mute respectively.

Special Tunings
Non-standard tunings are shown as 'tuning boxes'. Each box represents one guitar string, the leftmost box corresponding to the lowest pitched string. The symbol '•' in a box means the pitch of the corresponding string is not altered. A note within a box means the string must be re-tuned as stated. For tablature readers, numbers appear in the boxes. The numbers represent the number of half-steps the string must be tuned up or down. The tablature relates to an instrument tuned as stated.

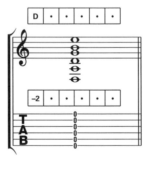

Tune the low E (6th) string down one tone (two half-steps) to D.

Chord naming
The following chord naming convention has been used:

Where there is no appropriate chord box, for example when the music consists of a repeated figure (or riff) the tonal base is indicated in parenthesis: **[C]**

Where it was not possible to transcribe a passage, the symbol ∿ appears.

Indications sur la notation musicale et les tablatures

Accord de Do majeur ouvert

Gamme de Mi majeur

Mi aigu: 1ère corde
Si: 2e corde
Sol: 3e corde
Ré: 4e corde
La: 5e corde
Mi grave: 6e corde

Bending

La note correspondant à la case sur laquelle on pose le doigt est toujours indiquée en premier. Les variations de hauteur sont obtenues en poussant sur la corde et sont indiquées par le symbole: ⌐ ¬. En cas de doute sur la hauteur à atteindre, le fait de jouer les notes indiquées sans pousser sur la corde permet de trouver ensuite la bonne hauteur. Les examples suivants démontrent les techniques de bending les plus courantes.

Exemple 1
Jouez la note Ré et poussez la corde d'un ton (deux demi-tons) pour atteindre le Mi.

Exemple 4
'Pre-bend': posez le doigt sur la case de Ré, poussez d'un ton pour atteindre le Mi avant de jouer la note.

Exemple 2
Jouez le Ré, poussez sur la corde pour atteindre le Mi un ton plus haut, relâchez ensuite pour revenir au Ré. Seule la première note est jouée avec le médiator.

Exemple 5
Jouez La et Ré simultanément; poussez ensuite sur la corde de Si pour atteindre la note Si.

Exemple 3
'Fast Bend': jouez le Ré et poussez le plus rapidement possible pour atteindre le Mi.

Exemple 6
Jouez Ré et Fa♯ simultanément; poussez la corde de Sol d'un ton vers le Mi, et la corde de Si d'un demi-ton vers le Sol.

D'autres techniques de guitare sont notées de la façon suivante:

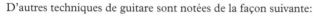

Emploi du levier de vibrato
Modifiez la hauteur du son avec le levier de vibrato. Lorsque c'est possible, la note à atteindre est indiquée.
a) Jouez le Sol et appuyez sur le levier de vibrato pour atteindre le Mi.
b) Jouez un Sol à vide et détendez le plus possible la corde avec le levier de vibrato pour rendre un effect de 'bombe qui tombe' (divebomb).

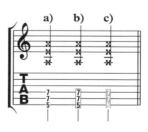

Mutes (étouffements)
a) Mute de la main droite
Etouffez en posant la main droite sur les cordes, au-dessus du chevalet.
b) Mute de la main gauche
Relâchez la pression sur la corde juste après avoir joué la note.
c) Mute sans hauteur définie
Etouffez les cordes avec la main gauche pour obtenir un son de percussion.

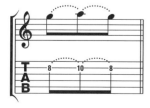

Hammer On et Pull Off
Jouez la première note; frappez la corde sur la touche (Hammer On) pour obtenir la seconde note, et relâchez la seconde note en tirant sur la corde (Pull Off) pour obtenir la troisième note. Seule la première note est done jouée avec le médiator.

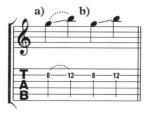

Glissando
a) Jouez la première note avec le médiator, faites sonner la seconde note en ne faisant que glisser le doigt sur la corde.
b) Comme ci-dessus, mais en attaquant également la seconde note avec le médiator.

Harmoniques naturelles

Posez le doigt sur la corde au dessus de la barrette indiquée, et jouez avec le médiator pour obtenir un son cristallin. Le cas échéant, une petite note indique la hauteur du son que l'on doit obtenir.

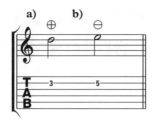

Guitare Slide

a) Note jouée avec le slide.
b) Note jouée sans le slide.

Harmoniques artificielles

Posez le doigt (main gauche) sur la note la plus basse: effleurez la corde avec l'index de la main droite au-dessus de la barrette indiquée par la note en forme de losange, tout en actionnant le médiator. La petite note indique la hauteur du son que l'on doit obtenir.

Effet de Vibrato

Jouez le vibrato soit avec le doigt sur la corde (main gauche), soit avec le levier de vibrato. Comme le vibrato est une affaire de technique et de goût personnels, il n'est indiqué que quand cela est vraiment nécessaire.

Harmoniques pincées

Appuyez le doigt sur la corde de la façon habituelle, mais utilisez conjointement le médiator et l'index de la main droite de façon á obtenir une harmonique aiguë. Les petites notes indiquent la hauteur du son que l'on doit obtenir.

Scratch

Faites glisser le médiator du haut en bas de la corde. Le meilleur effet est obtenu avec des cordes filetées.

Quarts de ton

Une flèche dirigée vers le bas indique que la note est baissée d'un quart-de-ton. Une flèche dirigée vers le haut indique que la note est haussée d'un quart-de-ton.

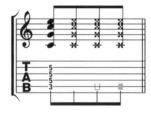

Accords répétés

Pour faciliter la lecture des parties de guitare rythmique, les chiffres de tablature sont omis quand l'accord est répété. L'example montre successivement un accord de Do majeur joué de façon normale, un 'mute' de la main droite, un 'mute' de la main gauche et un 'mute' sans hauteur définie.

Accordages spéciaux

Les accordages non-standards sont indiqués par six cases, chacune représentant une corde (de gauche à droite), de la plus grave à la plus aiguë. Un tiret indique que la tension de la corde correspondante ne doit pas être altérée. Un nom de note indique la nouvelle note à obtenir. Pour les tablatures, les chiffres indiqués dans les cases représentent le nombre de demi-tons dont ou doit désaccorder la corde, vers le haut ou vers le bas.

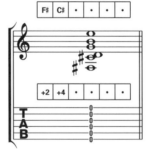

Accordez la corde de Mi grave un ton plus haut de façon à obtenir un Fa♯, et la corde de La deux tons plus haut de façon à obtenir un Do♯.

Noms des accords

Lorsqu'aucun nom d'accord précis n'est applicable, par exemple quand la musique consiste en une figure répétée (riff), le centre tonal est indiqué entre parenthèses: [C]

Lorsqu'un passage n'a pas pu être transcrit, le symbole ∿ apparait.

Hinweise zu Notation und Tabulatur

Offener C - Dur - Akkord

E - Dur - Tonleiter

Hohe E-Saite (1.)
H-Saite (2.)
G-Saite (3.)
D-Saite (4.)
A-Saite (5.)
Tiefe E-Saite (6.)

Gezogene Noten

Die gegriffene Note wird immer zuerst angegeben. Das Zeichen ⌐ ¬ zeigt eine Veränderung der Tonhöhe an, die durch das Ziehen der Saiten erreicht wird. Falls Du nicht sicher bist, wie weit die Saite gezogen werden soll, spiele die entsprechenden Töne zunächst ohne Ziehen; so kannst Du Dich an der Tonhöhe orientieren. Die folgenden Beispiele geben die gebräuchlichsten Techniken zum Ziehen wieder:

Beispiel 1
Spiele das D und ziehe dann um einen Ton (zwei Halbtonschritte) höher zum E.

Beispiel 4
Im Voraus gezogen: Greife das D, ziehe um einen Ton höher zum E und schlage erst dann die Saite an.

Beispiel 2
Spiele das D, ziehe um einen Ton hoch zum E und dann wieder zurück, so daß D erklingt. Dabei wird nur die erste Note angeschlagen.

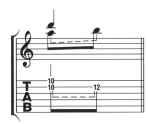

Beispiel 5
Spiele A und D gleichzeitig und ziehe dann die H-Saite um einen Ton nach oben, so daß H erklingt.

Beispiel 3
Schnelles Ziehen: Spiele das D und ziehe dann so schnell Du kannst um einen Ton höher zum E.

Beispiel 6
Spiele D und Fis gleichzeitig; ziehe dann die G-Saite um einen Ton nach oben zum E und die H-Saite um einen Halbtonschritt nach oben zum G.

Zusätzliche Spieltechniken für Gitarre wurden folgendermaßen notiert:

Tremolo
Verändere die Tonhöhe mit dem Tremolo-Hebel. Wenn es möglich ist, wird die angestrebte Tonhöhe angezeigt.
a) Spiele G; nutze den Takt, um zum E abzusteigen.
b) Spiele die leere G-Saite; nutze den Takt, um so weit wie möglich abzusteigen.

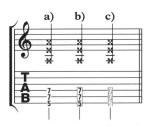

Dämpfen
a) Mit der rechten Hand
Dämpfe die Saiten, indem Du die rechte Hand einfach oberhalb der Brücke auf die Saiten legst.
b) Mit der linken Hand
Dämpfe die Saiten, indem Du den Druck der linken Hand löst, kurz nachdem die Töne erklingen.
c) Ohne bestimmte Tonhöhe
Dämpfe die Saiten mit der linken Hand; so erzielst Du einen 'geschlagenen' Sound.

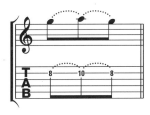

Hammer on und Pull off
Spiele die erste Note; die zweite erklingt durch 'Hammering on', die dritte durch 'Pulling off'. Dabei wird nur die erste Note angeschlagen.

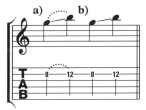

Glissando
a) Spiele die erste Note; die zweite erklingt durch Hochrutschen des Fingers auf der Saite. Nur die erste Note wird angeschlagen.
b) Wie oben, aber die zweite Note wird angeschlagen.

Natürliches Flageolett

Berühre die Saite über dem angegebenen Bund; wenn Du jetzt anschlägst, entsteht ein glockenähnlicher Ton. Wo es nötig ist, zeigen kleine Notenköpfe die entstandene Note an.

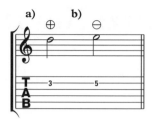

Slide Guitar

a) Spiele mit Rutschen des Fingers.
b) Spiele ohne Rutschen.

Künstliches Flageolett

Greife die unterste Note, berühre die Saite über dem durch Rauten angegebenen Bund und schlage dann den Ton an. Die kleinen Notenköpfe zeigen wieder die entstandene Note an.

Vibrato

Beim Vibrato läßt Du die Note für die Dauer eines Tons durch Druckvariation oder Tremolo-Hebel 'beben'. Da es jedoch eine Frage des persönlichen Geschmacks ist, wird Vibrato nur dort angegeben, wo es unerläßlich ist.

Gezupftes Flageolett

Greife die Note ganz normal, aber drücke die Saite mit der zupfenden Hand so, daß ein harmonischer Oberton entsteht. Kleine Notenköpfe zeigen den entstandenen Ton an.

Pick Scratch

Fahre mit dem Plektrum nach unten über die Saiten – das klappt am besten bei umsponnenen Saiten.

Vierteltöne

Ein nach unten gerichteter Pfeil bedeutet, daß die notierte Tonhöhe um einen Viertelton erniedrigt wird; ein nach oben gerichteter Pfeil bedeutet, daß die notierte Tonhöhe um einen Viertelton erhöht wird.

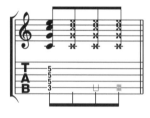

Akkordwiederholung

Um die Stimmen für Rhythmus-Gitarre leichter lesbar zu machen, werden die Tabulaturziffern weggelassen, wenn ein Akkord wiederholt werden soll. Unser Beispiel zeigt einen C - Dur - Akkord normal gespielt, rechts gedämpft, links gedämpft und ohne Tonhöhe.

Besondere Stimmung

Falls eine Stimmung verlangt wird, die vom Standard abweicht, wird sie in Kästchen angegeben. Jedes Kästchen steht für eine Saite, das erste links außen entspricht der tiefsten Saite. Wenn die Tonhöhe einer Saite nicht verändert werden soll, enthält das Kästchen einen Punkt. Steht eine Note im Kästchen, muß die Saite wie angegeben umgestimmt werden. In der Tabulaturschrift stehen stattdessen Ziffern im entsprechenden Kästchen: Sie geben die Zahl der Halbtonschritte an, um die eine Saite höher oder tiefer gestimmt werden soll.

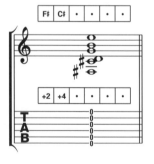

Stimme die tiefe E-Saite (6.) um einen Ganzton (zwei Halbtonschritte) höher auf Fis und die A-Saite (5.) um zwei Ganztöne (vier Halbtonschritte) höher auf Cis.

Akkordbezeichnung

Die folgenden Akkordbezeichnungen wurden verwendet.

Wenn kein eigenes Akkordsymbol angegeben ist, z.B. bei Wiederholung einer musikalischen Figur (bzw. Riff), steht die Harmoniebezeichnung in Klammern: [C]

Das Symbol ∼ steht jeweils dort, wo es nicht möglich war, einen Abschnitt zu übertragen.

Spiegazione della notazione e dell'intavolatura

Accordo di Do aperto
(in prima posizione)

Scala di Mi maggiore

Mi acuto: la corda
Si: 2a corda
Sol: 3a corda
Re: 4a corda
La: 5a corda
Mi basso: 6a corda

Bending

La prima nota scritta è sempre quella tastata normalmente. Le alterazioni di altezza da realizzare con la trazione laterale della corda (bending) interessano le note comprese sotto al segno: ⌐ ⌐. Se siete incerti sull'entità dell'innalzamento di tono da raggiungere, suonate le note indicate tastando normalmente la corda. Gli esempi seguenti mostrano le tecniche più comunemente impiegate nella maggior parte dei casi che possono presentarsi.

Esempio 1
Suonate il Re e innalzate di un tono (due mezzi toni) a Mi.

Esempio 4
'Pre-Bend': tastate il Re, tirate alzando di un tono a Mi e poi suonate.

Esempio 2
Suonate il Re, tirate alzando di un tono a Mi e rilasciate tornando a Re. Va suonata solo la prima nota.

Esempio 5
Suonate simultaneamente La e Si quindi tirate la 2a corda per innalzare il suono a Si.

Esempio 3
'Bend Veloce': suonate il Re e quindi alzate di un tono a Mi il più velocemente possibile.

Esempio 6
Suonate simultaneamente Re e Fa# quindi tirate la 3a corda alzando il suono di un tono a Mi, e la 2a corda di mezzo tono, alzando il suono a Sol.

Negli esempi seguenti sono illustrate altre tecniche chitarristiche:

Barra del tremolo
Alterate l'altezza del suono mediante la barra del tremolo. Dove possibile l'altezza da raggiungere è indicata.
a) Suonate il Sol e abbassate il suono fino a Mi mediante la barra.
b) Suonate il Sol a vuoto e scendete quanto più possibile.

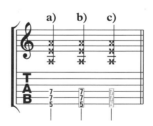

Smorzato
a) Smorzato con la destra
Smorzare le corde con il palmo della mano destra in prossimità del ponticello.
b) Smorzato con la sinistra
Smorzare le corde allentando la pressione delle dita subito dopo aver prodotto i suoni.
c) Pizzicato
Premere leggermente le corde in modo che non producano note ma soltanto un effetto percussivo.

Legature ascendenti e discendenti
Suonate la prima nota e ricavate la seconda percuotendo la corda con il dito contro la barretta; per la terza nota tirate la corda con il medesimo dito. Soltano la prima nota va suonata.

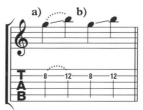

Glissando
a) Suonate la prima nota e ricavare la seconda facendo scivolare il dito lungo la corda. Va pizzicata solo la prima nota.
b) Come sopra, ma pizzicando anche la seconda nota.

Armonici naturali

Toccate leggermente la corda sulla barretta indicata e pizzicate col plettro per produrre un suono di campana. Le notine indicano il suono risultante, dove occorra.

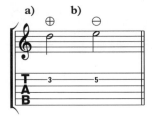

Slide Chitarra

a) Suonare con slide.
b) Suonare senza slide.

Armonici artificiali

Tastate la nota più bassa, toccate leggermente la corda sulla barretta relativa alla nota romboidale e pizzicate con il plettro. Le notine indicano il suono risultante.

Vibrato

Effettuate il vibrato facendo oscillare il dito che preme la corda oppure con la barra del tremolo. Poichè il vibrato è un fatto di gusto personale, viene indicato solo dove è essenziale.

Armonici pizzicati

Tastate normalmente la nota ma pizzicate la corda con la mano destra per ricavare l'armonico sopracuto. Le notine indicano l'altezza del suono risultante.

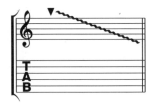

Suono graffiato

Fate scorrere il bordo del plettro lungo la corda. L'effetto è maggiore sulle corde fasciate.

Microintervalli

Una freccia diretta verso il basso significa che il suono scritto va abbassato di un intervallo inferiore al semitono; una freccia diretta verso l'alto innalza il suono scritto.

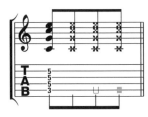

Accordi ripetuti

Per facilitare la lettura, possono venire omessi i numeri nell'intavolatura di un accordo ripetuto. L'esempio mostra un accordi di Do maggiore suonato normalmente, smorzato con la destra, smorzato con la sinistra e pizzicato (muto).

Accordature Speciali

Le accordature diverse da quella normale sono indicate in speciali 'gabbie di accordatura'. Ogni gabbia rappresenta una corda di chitarra; all'estremità sinistra corrisponde la corda più bassa. Il simbolo '•' in una gabbia sta ad indicare che l'intonazione della corda corrispondente è quella normale. Una nota nella gabbia indica che l'intonazione di quella corda va modificata portandola all'altezza indicata. Per coloro che leggono l'intavolatura, dei numeri posti nelle gabbie stanno ad indicare di quanti semitoni deve salire o scendere l'intonazione della corda. L'intavolatura è da considerarsi relativa ad uno strumento accordato come indicato nelle gabbie.

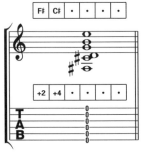

Accordate la corda del Mi basso (6a) un tono sopra (due semitoni) a Fa#. Accordate la corda del La basso (5a) due toni sopra (quattro semitoni) a Do#.

Indicazione degli accordi

E' stata impiegata la seguente nomenclatura convenzionale degli accordi.

Quando non compare la griglia appropriata di un accordo, ad esempio, quando la musica consiste nella ripetizione di una stessa figura (riff), la base tonale è indicata fra parentesi: [C]

Printed in England

Dove non è stato possibile trascivere il passaggio, compare il segno ∼ .